MUSIC QUIZ

Project Book

Test your music knowledge with this quiz.

5 games inside

INTRODUCTION

"Music gives soul to the universe, wings to the mind, flight to the imagination and life to everything." – Plato

This kit has been designed specifically for adults only.

It really is true, music does make the world go round. But how much do you really know? Maybe you're one of those people who thinks you know a lot about music. Well, now is your chance to prove it!

Test your knowledge and take your rightful place in the musical Hall of Fame as the reigning champion of your friends and family. This all round quiz has everything from Amy Winehouse to Iron Maiden, and will really push your musical boundaries. What you don't know, you're about to learn.

So, what are you waiting for?

There are 5 games for you to play:

- •General knowledge
- •Snap
- •True or false
- •Song titles that...
- •Quick fire

KIT CONTENTS

WHAT'S INCLUDED:

·Trivia cards
·Score sheets
·Spinner
·Paddles

WHAT YOU'LL NEED:

·Friends or family
·Fighting spirit
·A sharp mind!
......oh, and a pen.

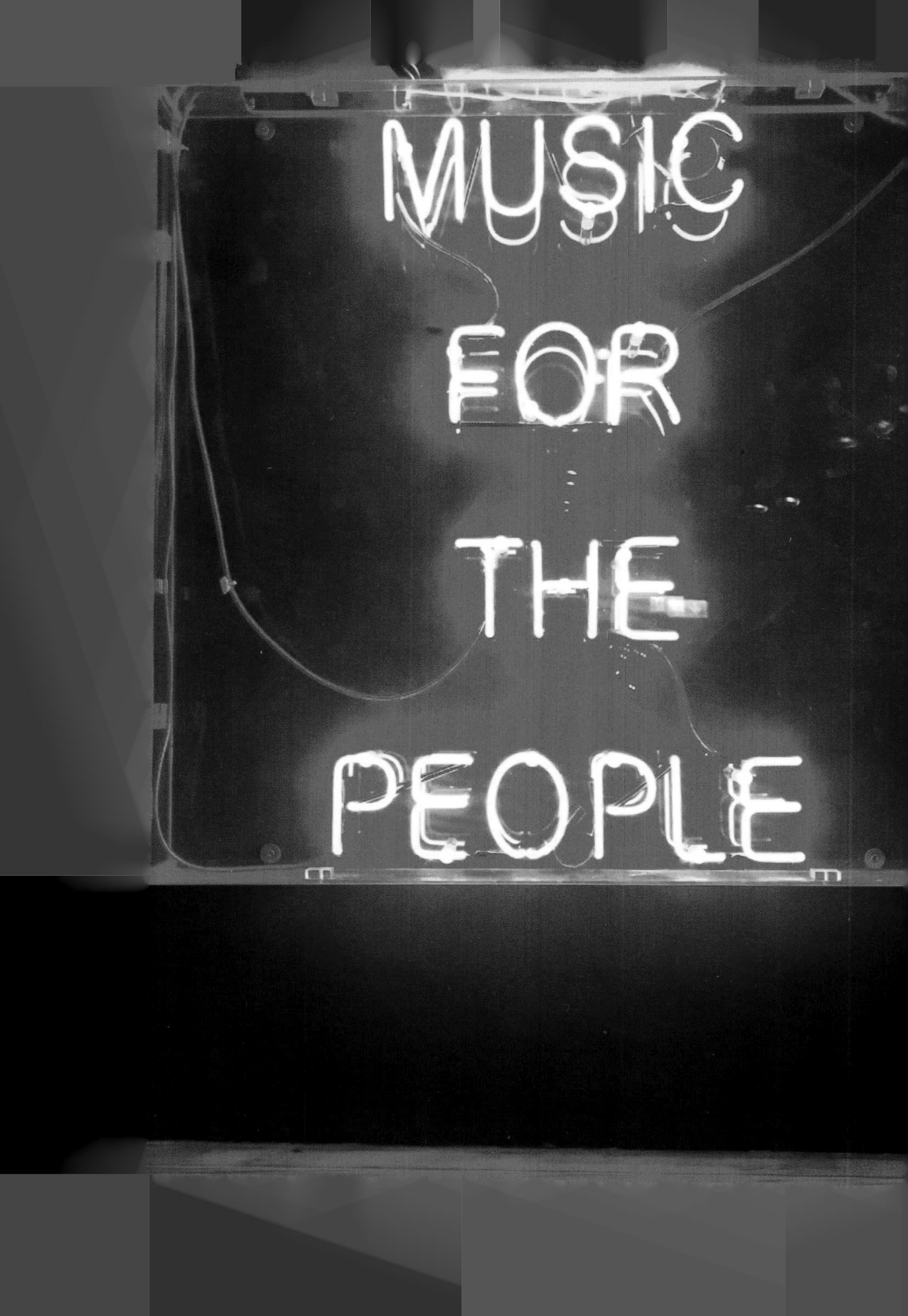
MUSIC
FOR
THE
PEOPLE

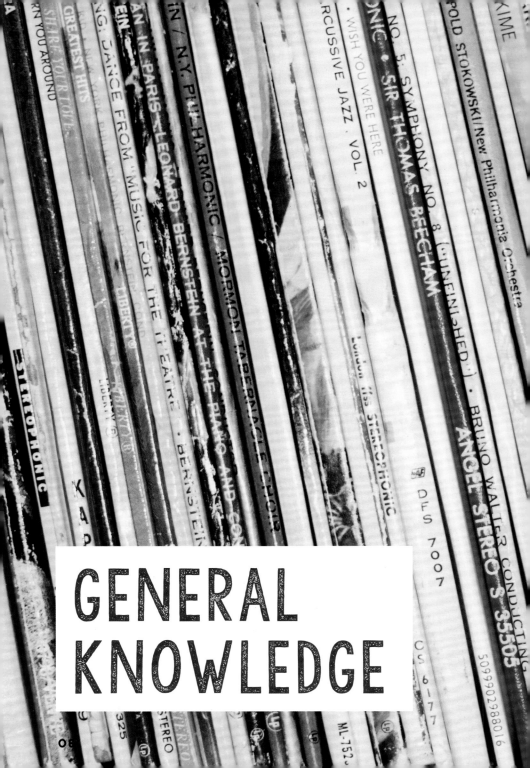

GENERAL KNOWLEDGE

GENERAL KNOWLEDGE

Test your musical prowess with this general knowledge quiz! Let's Go! It's time to think of a witty team name and press **PLAY!** on this game.

HOW TO PLAY

1. First, split into teams and grab a score sheet. Write your team name on the sheet - (don't forget to make it funny!)

Thin Quizzies!

The Tina Turntables!

SCORES		Round 1	Round 2	Round 3
Team	Round Total			
	Game Total			
Team	Round Total			
	Game Total			
Team	Round Total			
	Game Total			
Team	Round Total			
	Game Total			
Team	Round Total			
	Game Total			

Music Quiz

2. You can either play with just the 'general knowledge' cards or, if you want to spice things up, add in two of the other mini games. To do this, you can use the spinner to alternate between categories.

3. The team whose turn it is spins the spinner – make sure it lands clearly on a category (no cheating!)

*Illustration purposes only!

4. An opposing team then reads the card from the category. (If it lands on true or false? get your paddles at the ready!)

AND WIN THOSE POINTS!

Paddles

True

False

ARTISTS

Ever wondered where some of greatest bands and musicians in the world originated? Here we explore some of the UK's best!

ENGLAND:

Amy Winehouse - Enfield, London
Blur - London
Queen - London
The Rolling Stones - London
Wolf Alice - London
Pink Floyd - London
David Bowie - Brixton, London
Mumford and Sons - London
Kate Bush - Welling, London
The Sex Pistols - London
The Clash - London
The Who - London
Led Zeppelin - London
Elton John - Pinner, London
Dua Lipa - London
George Michael - East Finchley, London
Stormzy - Croydon, London
Anne-Marie - East Tilbury, Essex
The Smiths - Manchester
Dizzee Rascal - Bow, London
Radiohead - Oxfordshire
Harry Styles - Redditch
Duran Duran - Birmingham
Joy Division - Salford
Oasis - Manchester
The Beatles - Liverpool
Pulp - Sheffield
Ed Sheeran - West Yorkshire
The Libertines - London
Arctic Monkeys - Sheffield
The Cure - Crawley, West Sussex
Black Sabbath - Birmingham
Iron Maiden - London
The Wombats - Liverpool

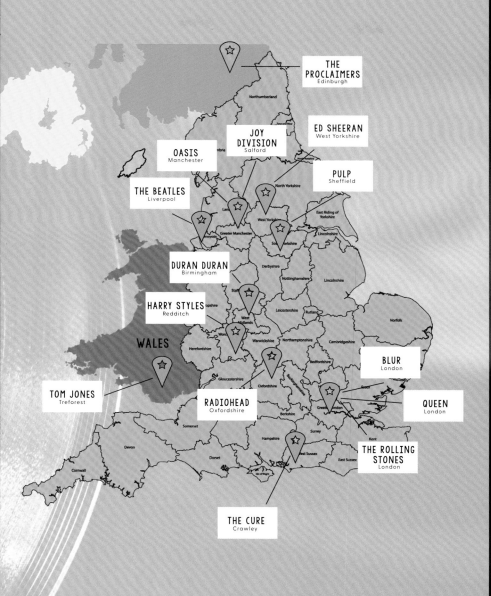

THE PROCLAIMERS
Edinburgh

ED SHEERAN
West Yorkshire

JOY DIVISION
Salford

OASIS
Manchester

PULP
Sheffield

THE BEATLES
Liverpool

DURAN DURAN
Birmingham

HARRY STYLES
Redditch

WALES

TOM JONES
Treforest

RADIOHEAD
Oxfordshire

BLUR
London

QUEEN
London

THE ROLLING STONES
London

THE CURE
Crawley

LET IT BE

13

SNAP!

SNAP!

Are you quick enough!?

HOW TO PLAY

For a minimum of 2+ Players

1. Separate your 'SNAP!' cards from the rest of the deck.

2. . You know the drill! Fastest wins!
Take it in turns to put a card down until they match! First person to shout 'SNAP!' (or a word of your choice) wins!

FESTIVALS

- In 1970, a dairy farmer by the name of Michael Eavis CBE, started the first Glastonbury Festival with tickets costing £1 – including free milk from the farm. It was held the day after Jimi Hendrix died and had an attendance of 1,500 people. Rather than 'Glastonbury', it was called the 'Pilton Festival' with acts including; Marc Bolan, Keith Christmas and Al Stewart. It has continued to be held at Eavis' 150-acre farm in Somerset, England for the last 37 years. Glastonbury Festival is world-renowned and has grown from 1,500 people to around 175,000 people each year.

- Woodstock Music & Art Fair, 1969, is often considered the first modern music festival and was set on 600-acres of farmland in New York. More than 100,000 tickets were sold, but nearly half a million people turned up!
Jimi Hendrix was one of the headline acts, and was paid $18,000 (the most out of all performers). His Sunday night headline set was delayed by technical issues and bad weather until 9am the next morning.
Other acts included; Janis Joplin, Grateful Dead, Joe Cocker and Crosby, Stills, Nash and Young.
It ran on for four days instead of the scheduled three.

- Summerfest is the world's largest music festival and is based in the USA. It attracts between 800,000 and 1,000,000 people each year, with more than 800 acts and 1,000 performances over 11 days.

- SnowGlobe Music Festival is an outdoor festival held in the snow in South Lake Tahoe, USA. It takes place in the three days leading up to New Year's Eve.

- Download festival, UK, is a rock and metal festival that first launched in 2003. It is held at Donington Park, Leicestershire and has had headliners from System of a Down, Aerosmith, Guns 'N' Roses and Slipknot.

- Reading and Leeds festival, UK, originally started as The National Jazz and Blues festival in 1961 by Harold Pendleton. It moved to several locations before settling in Reading. It was the late 70's when the music started to turn to a more punk vibe.

In 1999, Leeds was added as a second location! 2019 saw a record number of festival goers, reaching heights of 105,000!

- According to Guinness World Records, the largest festival attendance took place in Vienna, Austria, in 2015 known as the Danube Island Festival. During the three days, more than 3.3 million people turned up! That's more than the population of Iceland, Alaska, Vermont and Wyoming combined!

- For most students, just graduating is an accomplishment in itself, but in Novi Sad, Serbia, a couple of students organised the first EXIT festival in the city's University Park in 2000. It was born out of political activism - protesting for democracy and freedom in Serbia and the Balkans. It's now an award-winning EXIT festival.
Unfortunately, the 20th anniversary plans were put on hold due to Covid-19, but they were able to celebrate back in July 2021.

- The most remote festival in the world is considered to be Australia's Birdsville Big Red Bash in the Simpson Desert, Queensland.

TRUE OR FALSE?

TRUE OR FALSE?

Can you tell the fact from fiction and become victorious!?

HOW TO PLAY

For a minimum of 2+ Players

1. Split into two teams. Separate out the 'True or False?' cards from the deck.

2. Pick a card to read to your opponent.
On each card is a statement. They will have to decide whether it is true or false! Simple, right?

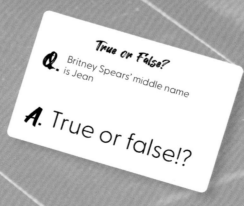

3. Use the paddles to choose your answer!

Do you know the truth?

SONG TITLES
THAT...

SONG TITLES THAT...

Think you can name 5 titles with the word 'love' in?
Or name 5 titles featuring a name? Let's find out!

HOW TO PLAY

For a minimum of 2+ Players

1. Split into two teams. Separate out the 'Song titles that...' cards from the deck.

2. Pick a card to read to your opponent.
On each card is a category. You can make your own rules on how you would like to play.
You can either choose to name a certain amount of song titles, (e.g. name 5 songs with the word 'love' in the title) or you can name just one song. Alternatively, bounce between teams. The last one standing wins the points.

Song titles that.....

contain
girl's names

How many can you name?

HALL OF FAME

Frank Sinatra

Francis Albert Sinatra was an American swing singer and actor, and considered the first 'pop star'. Born December 12, 1915 – May 14, 1998, he was one of the best-selling artists of all time, with around 150 million records bought worldwide. Although he was a solo artist, he did go on to sing with The Rat Pack in the early 50's. His best-selling song spent 75 weeks in the top 40.

Ella Fitzgerald

Ella Fitzgerald was an American jazz singer born in April 1917 - 1996 and was known as the 'First Lady of Song', 'Queen of Jazz' and 'Lady Ella'.
Frank Sinatra once said that Ella Fitzgerald was the best singer he had ever heard, and the only one who made him nervous to sing with.
She came from a humble and sometimes, difficult background, but felt at home in the spotlight.
Even though she was popular, she still suffered discrimination from the public and the police.

Elvis Presley

Elvis Aaron Presley was an American singer and actor born in January 1935 - 1977. He was known as the "King of Rock and Roll" and is one of the most iconic musicians of the 20th century.
Before launching his music career in 1954, he grew up in a poor household and drove a truck.
In 1957, aged 23, Elvis was drafted into the army, even though he was already famous, where he served for two years.
His voice, looks and dance moves made him one of the world most acclaimed musicians.

Freddie Mercury

Freddie Mercury, known as the frontman for rock band, Queen, was a British singer-songwriter. Along with his powerful stage presence, which is famously shown in Queen's Live Aid performance in 1985, he was considered one of the greatest rock vocalists.

Freddy once said that his mum would 'freak out' at some of his outfit choices, worrying that their neighbours may see him. It was that sort of artistic flair and expression that made him so popular.

He also designed the Queen logo based on the bands star signs, two lions for Leo, crab for Cancer and two fairies for Freddy's Virgo.

Their biggest hit, happens to be the biggest selling hit of all time in the UK.

David Bowie

David Robert Jones was born in 1947 in London. He died in 2016 in New York. He was known for his incredible changes in style throughout his music career, based on different personas - Ziggy Stardust, Aladdin Sane, Halloween Jack, the Thin White Duke, and the Blind Prophet.

One of Bowie's songs, which was also his first UK hit, was used when the BBC covered the moon landing in 1969.

Beatles

Formed in Liverpool, UK, The Beatles were world renowned for their amazing music. They started their music career in the 1960's and have topped the UK charts with more than 15 albums as well as receiving fifteen Ivor Novello Awards from the British Academy of Songwriters, Composers and Authors. They are one of the most famous bands in the world to this day!

QUICK FIRE

QUICK FIRE

A quick fire round, but which one of you will burn up first!

HOW TO PLAY

For a minimum of 2+ Players

This game requires nothing but a score sheet and pen.

1. Pick a direction and starting point in your group!

2. Pick a category from;

- Singers and bands
- Songs
- Albums
- Instruments

3. Once you have your category, pick a random letter and start from the first person. Continue until one of you fails to come up with an answer or repeats an already given answer.

For example:

Category – Bands and singers beginning with the letter 'F'.

QUIZ

This is a Music Quiz kit after all! Let's see if you have done your homework. All the answers are hidden somewhere in the booklet. So, let's see what you've got!

1. Where is the metal and rock festival, Download, held in the UK?

_____

2. What city was Amy Winehouse from?

_____

3. What was Elvis Presley also known as?

_____

4. Who designed Queen's logo?

_____

5. ...And what was it based on?

_____

6. Which city were The Beatles from?

_____

7. What group did Frank Sinatra sing with in the early 50's?

_____

8. What happened to Elvis Presley when he turned 23?

_____

9. In 1969, what did the BBC use David Bowie's song for?

_____

10. What era did Reading Festival change to punk music?

_____

11. Who said that Ella Fitzgerald was the best singer he had ever heard?

_____

CROSSWORD

Fill in the blank crossword. Not all of these artists are in the book, but I'm sure you can figure it out! Good luck!

Down

1. Tina _____
3. _____ Fitzgerald
4. Ed _____
6. _____ Cat

Across

2. _____ Grande
3. _____ Presley
5. _____ Styles
7. _____ Swift

CROSSWORD

Down

1. Frank _____
3. Anne - _____
4. _____ Gaga
5. Beastie _____

Across

2. _____ 'N' Roses
4. _____ Del Rey
5. _____ Eilish
6. Olivia _____

WORDSEARCH

P	O	P	F	Y	R	B	P	A
Y	U	G	T	S	O	U	L	L
S	P	L	K	R	C	S	W	T
W	R	P	U	N	K	M	N	E
I	P	O	H	R	F	L	Q	R
N	L	M	K	H	L	I	R	N
G	H	I	E	F	K	S	E	A
E	R	U	H	T	Q	E	V	T
D	T	A	D	K	A	U	D	I
I	D	F	P	A	V	L	H	V
S	B	D	B	K	J	B	L	E
D	A	N	C	E	W	O	E	C

POP ✓   SWING ✓   SOUL
PUNK   BLUES ✓   ALTERNATIVE
ROCK ✓   RAP
METAL   DANCE

WORDSEARCH

```
C  M  D  R  A  D  I  O  P
R  E  R  L  U  C  T  E  I
I  G  U  I  T  A  R  N  A
W  Y  M  A  G  S  W  O  N
S  L  O  P  E  S  T  H  O
B  A  S  S  U  E  S  P  Y
L  F  W  O  W  T  G  O  R
Y  L  U  E  A  T  E  R  D
N  U  O  F  S  E  D  C  O
I  T  V  C  I  U  W  I  P
V  E  M  D  V  R  E  M  G
G  W  N  K  R  N  K  F  E
```

DRUM   FLUTE   MICROPHONE
BASS   VINYL   CASSETTE
GUITAR   RADIO
PIANO   CD